FRANZ SCHUBERT

QUARTETTSATZ
QUARTET MOVEMENT

for 2 Violins, Viola and Violoncello
C minor/c-Moll/Ut mineur
D 703

Edited by/Herausgegeben von
Max Hochkofler

Ernst Eulenburg Ltd
London · Mainz · Madrid · New York · Paris · Tokyo · Toronto · Zürich

All rights reserved. No part of this publication may be reproduced, stored in a retrieval system, or transmitted in any form or by any means, electronic, mechanical, photocopying, recording or otherwise, without the prior written permission of Ernst Eulenburg Ltd., 48 Great Marlborough Street, London W1V 2BN.

Quartet

Franz Schubert, Op. posth.
1797-1828

4

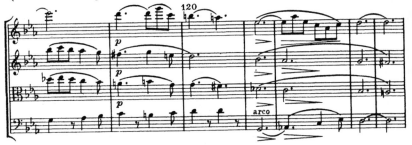

E. E. 3342